100 SOLOS
CLARINET

Arranged by Robin De Smet.

WISE PUBLICATIONS
LONDON/NEW YORK/PARIS/SYDNEY/COPENHAGEN/MADRID

EXCLUSIVE DISTRIBUTORS:
MUSIC SALES LIMITED
8/9 FRITH STREET. LONDON W1V 5TZ. ENGLAND.
MUSIC SALES PTY LIMITED
120 ROTHSCHILD AVENUE. ROSEBERY. NSW 2018. AUSTRALIA.

BOOK DESIGN BY PEARCE MARCHBANK STUDIO
PRINTED IN THE UNITED KINGDOM BY
REDWOOD BOOKS. TROWBRIDGE. WILTSHIRE.

THIS BOOK © COPYRIGHT 1983. 1993 BY
WISE PUBLICATIONS
ORDER NO. AM33689
ISBN 0-7119-0356-5

YOUR GUARANTEE OF QUALITY
AS PUBLISHERS. WE STRIVE TO PRODUCE EVERY BOOK TO THE HIGHEST COMMERCIAL STANDARDS.
THE BOOK HAS BEEN CAREFULLY DESIGNED TO MINIMISE AWKWARD PAGE TURNS
AND TO MAKE PLAYING FROM IT A REAL PLEASURE.
THROUGHOUT. THE PRINTING AND BINDING HAVE BEEN PLANNED TO ENSURE A STURDY.
ATTRACTIVE PUBLICATION WHICH SHOULD GIVE YEARS OF ENJOYMENT.
IF YOUR COPY FAILS TO MEET OUR HIGH STANDARDS. PLEASE INFORM US AND WE WILL GLADLY REPLACE IT.

MUSIC SALES' COMPLETE CATALOGUE DESCRIBES THOUSANDS OF TITLES AND
IS AVAILABLE IN FULL COLOUR SECTIONS BY SUBJECT. DIRECT FROM MUSIC SALES LIMITED.
PLEASE STATE YOUR AREAS OF INTEREST AND SEND A CHEQUE/POSTAL ORDER FOR £1.50 FOR POSTAGE TO:
MUSIC SALES LIMITED. NEWMARKET ROAD. BURY ST. EDMUNDS.
SUFFOLK IP33 3YB.

East Of The Sun (And West Of The Moon).
Words and Music by Brooks Bowman.

Pick A Pocket Or Two.
Words and Music by Lionel Bart.

Sailing.
Words and Music by Gavin Sutherland.

Slow Beat

Truly Scrumptious.
Words and Music by Richard M. Sherman and Robert B. Sherman.

Broadly

Morning Has Broken
Traditional

Amazing Grace

Traditional

Reviewing The Situation.

Words and Music by Lionel Bart.

Smile.
Words by John Turner & Geoffrey Parsons. Music by Charles Chaplin.

Andante

Greensleeves
Traditional

Moderato

Da Capo al Fine

Days Of Wine And Roses.

Words by Johnny Mercer. Music by Henry Mancini.

Moderato

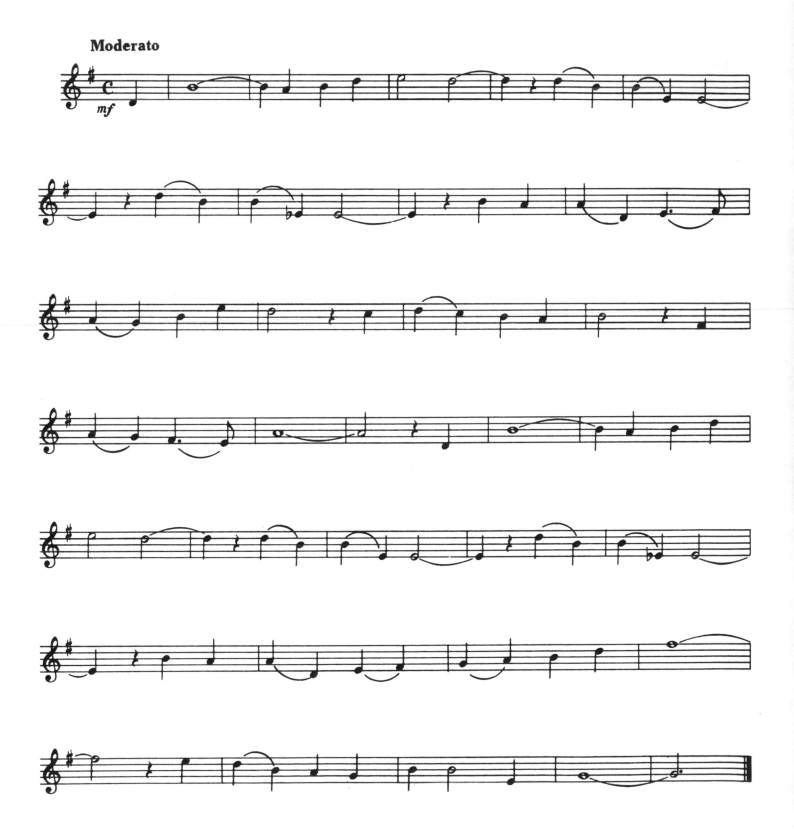

Never Smile At A Crocodile.

Words by Jack Lawrence. Music by Frank Churchill.

Moderately slow and liltingly

Paper Roses.
Words by Janice Torre. Music by Fred Spielman.

Moderately slow

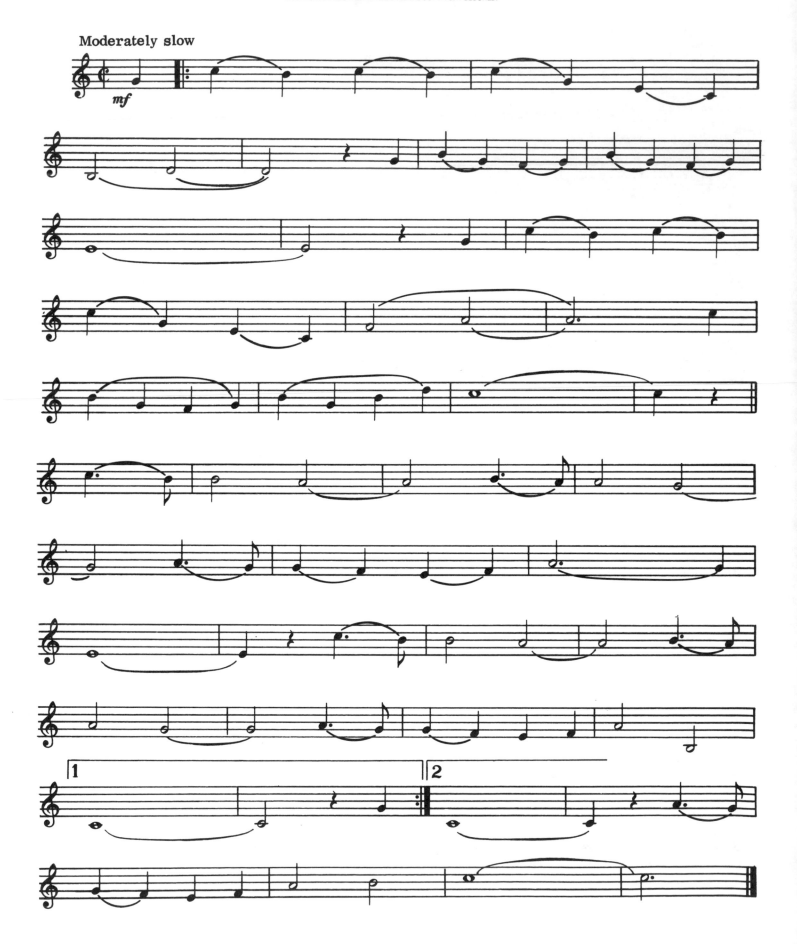

The Drunken Sailor
Traditional

Love Theme (from 'Romeo And Juliet').
Music by Peter Ilyich Tchaikovsky.

(Theme from) A Summer Place.
By Max Steiner.

She's Leaving Home.

Words and Music by John Lennon & Paul McCartney.

Moderato

Streets Of London.
Words and Music by Ralph McTell.

Moderately fast

When The Saints Go Marching In
Traditional

Quick march tempo

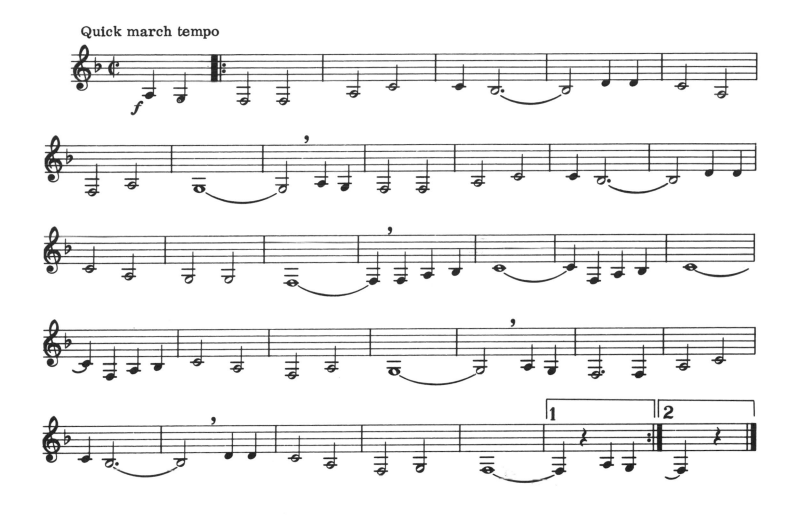

Shenandoah
Traditional

Flowingly

Strawberry Fields Forever.

Words and Music by John Lennon & Paul McCartney.

Be Back Soon.

Words and Music by Lionel Bart.

Supercalifragilisticexpialidocious.

Words and Music by Richard M. Sherman & Robert B. Sherman.

Somewhere My Love (Lara's Theme).

Words by Paul Francis Webster. Music by Mauric Jarre.

Who Do You Think You Are Kidding Mr. Hitler.

Words by Jimmy Perry. Music by Jimmy Perry & Derek Taverner.

Over The Rainbow.

Words by E. Y. Harburg. Music by Harold Arlen.

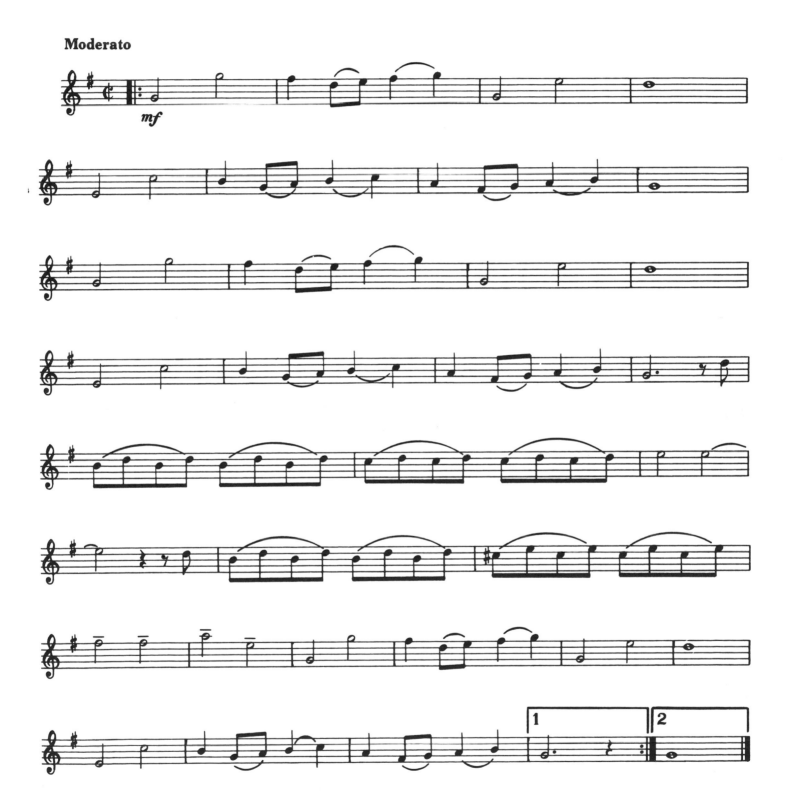

Consider Yourself.

Words and Music by Lionel Bart.

March tempo

An Apple For The Teacher.

Words by Johnny Burke. Music by James V. Monaco.

Little Brown Jug
Traditional

Lively

Whatever Will Be Will Be (Que Sera, Sera).

Words and Music by Jay Livingston and Ray Evans.

Moderate waltz

Take Me Home, Country Roads.

Words and Music by Bill Danoff, Taffy Nivert & John Denver.

Bright country beat

Oom Pah Pah.
Words and Music by Lionel Bart.

Cruising Down The River.

Words and Music by Eily Beadell & Nell Tollerton.

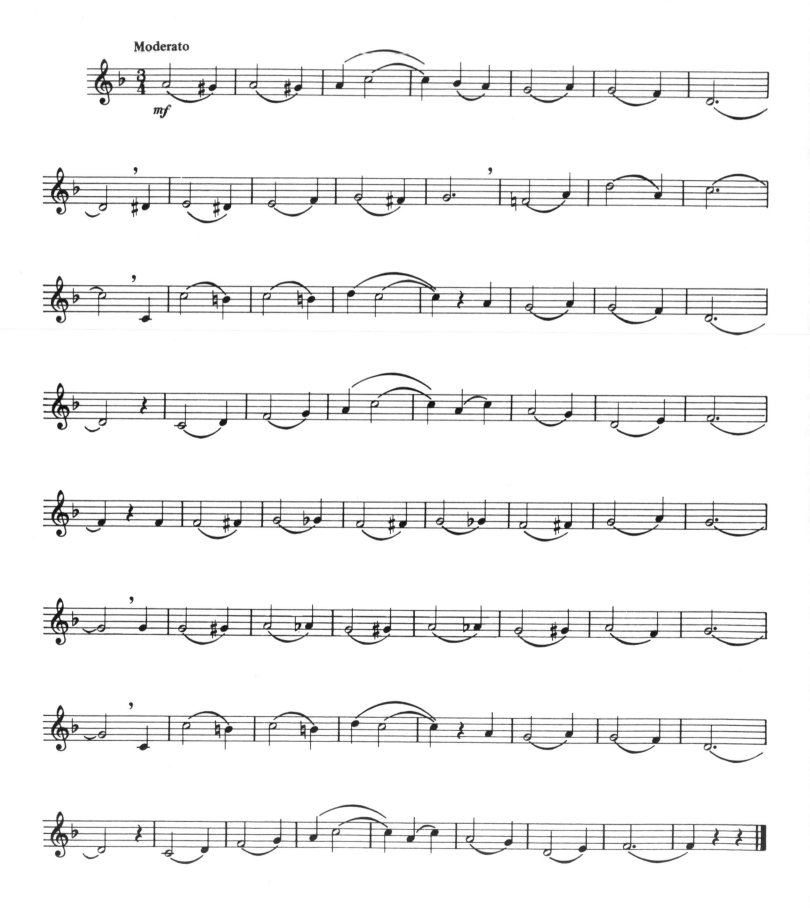

Ob-La-Di, Ob-La-Da.

Words and Music by John Lennon & Paul McCartney

Where Is Love.

Words and Music by Lionel Bart.

So Tired.

Words and Music by Russ Morgan & Jack Stuart.

Just For You.

Words and Music by Alan Price.

Sea Of Heartbreak.

Words and Music by Hal David & Paul Hampton.

Moderately bright

Moonlight Serenade.

Words by Mitchell Parish. Music by Glen Miller.

O Sole Mio.
Composed by E. Di Capua.

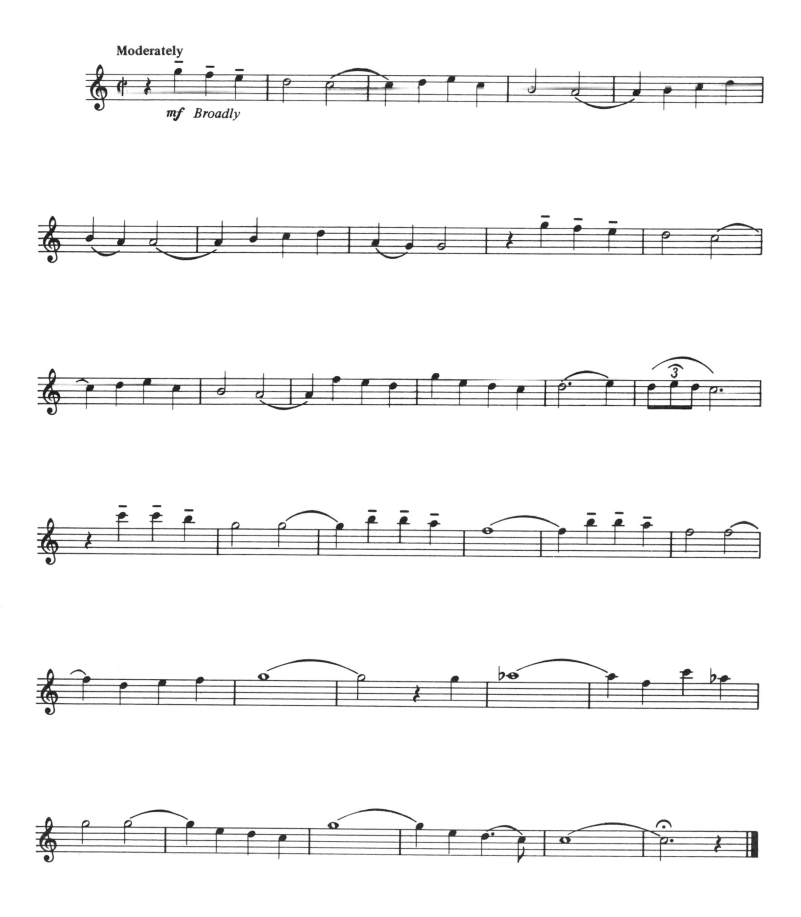

She Loves You.

Words and Music by John Lennon & Paul McCartney.

For Your Eyes Only.
Music by Bill Conti. Words by Michael Leeson.

See You Later Alligator.
Words and Music by Robert Guidry.

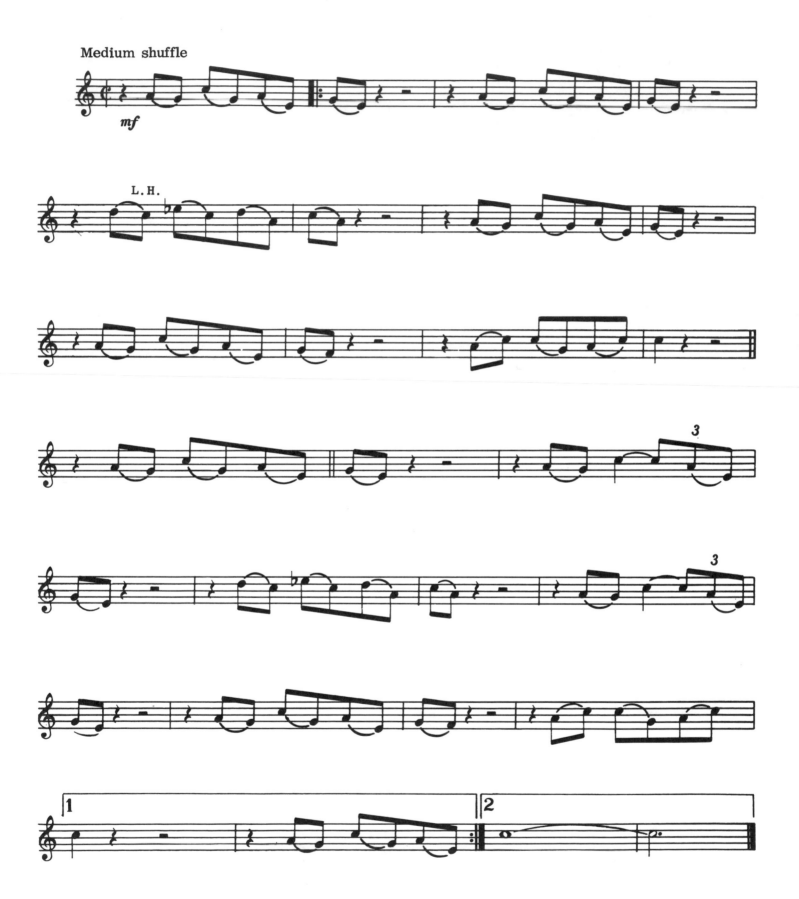

Louise.
Words by Leo Robin. Music by Richard A. Whiting.

The Green Leaves Of Summer.

Words by Paul Francis Webster. Music by Dimitri Tiomkin.

Love Is A Many Splendoured Thing.

Words by Paul Francis Webster. Music by Sammy Fain.

Moderato

As Long As He Needs Me.

Words and Music by Lionel Bart.

Moderato

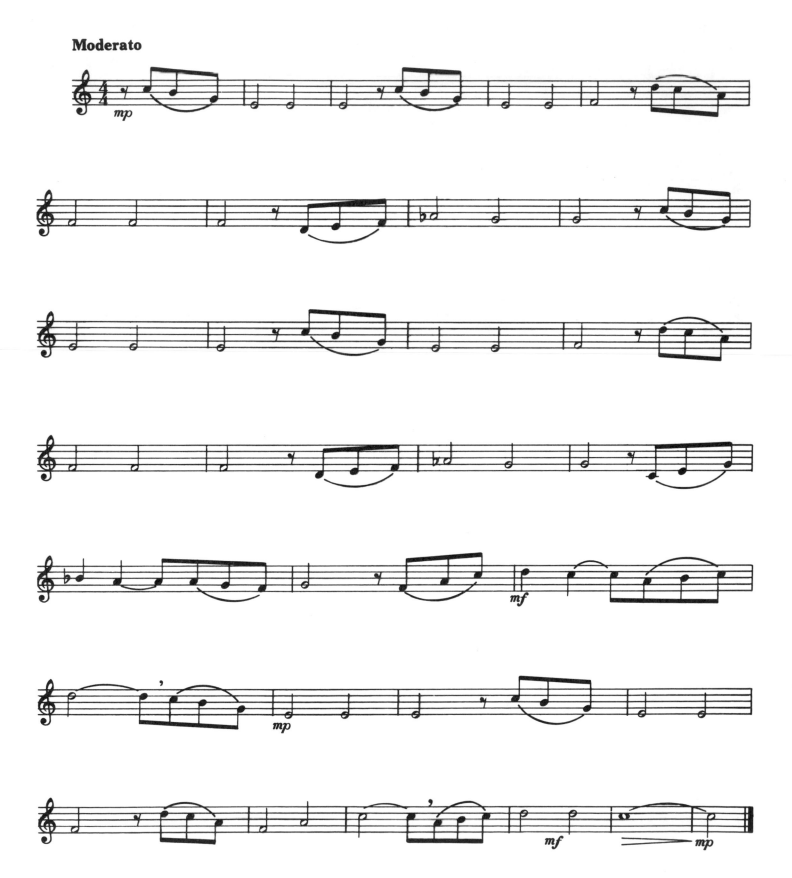

I'd Like To Teach The World To Sing.
Words and Music by Roger Cook, Roger Greenaway, Billy Backer & Billy Davis.

Moderato

D.S. al Fine

Michelle.

Words and Music by John Lennon & Paul McCartney.

Moderato

When I'm Sixty Four.
Words and Music by John Lennon & Paul McCartney.

Medium bounce

Steptoe And Son.
Music by Ron Grainer.

Moderato

Hi-Lili, Hi-Lo.
Words by Helen Deutsch. Music by Bronislau Kaper.

I Don't Know How To Love Him.

Music by Andrew Lloyd Webber. Lyrics by Tim Rice.

Kiss Me Honey-Honey (Kiss Me).
Words and Music by Al Timothy & Michael Julien.

The Rakes of Mallow (The Piper of Galway)
Traditional

English Country Garden.
Words and Music by Robert M. Jordan.

The Hawaiian Wedding Song.

Music and Original Hawaiian Lyric by Charles E. King. English Lyric by Al Hoffman & Dick Manning.

Bye Bye Baby.

Words by Leo Robin. Music by Jule Styne.

Norwegian Wood.
Words and Music by John Lennon & Paul McCartney.

All My Loving.
Words and Music by John Lennon & Paul McCartney.

Chitty Chitty Bang Bang.
Words and Music by Richard M. Sherman and Robert B. Sherman.

Bright tempo

Theme From Crossroads.

By Tony Hatch.

If I Were A Rich Man.

Words by Sheldon Harnick. Music by Jerry Bock.

I'm In The Mood For Love.

Words and Music by Jimmy McHugh & Dorothy Fields.

I'm Gettin' Sentimental Over You.

Words by Ned Washington. Music by Geo. Bassman.

Tulips From Amsterdam.

English words by Gene Martyn. Original words by Neumann & Bader. Music by Ralf Arnie

Quick Waltz tempo

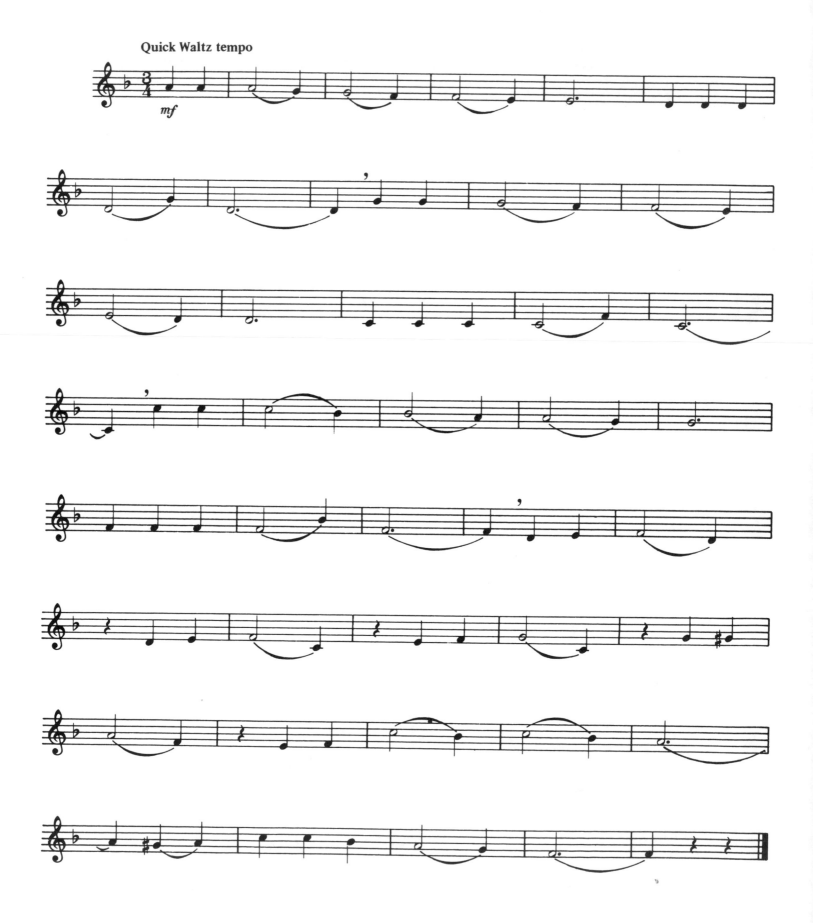

Don't Cry For Me Argentina.

Music by Andrew Lloyd Webber. Lyrics by Tim Rice.

Nellie The Elephant.

Words by Ralph Butler. Music by Peter Hart.

Deep Purple.

Words by Mitchell Parish. Music by Peter de Rose.

Because Of You.
Words and Music by Arthur Hammerstein & Dudley Wilkinson.

All I Do Is Dream Of You.

Words by Arthur Freed. Music by Nacio Herb Brown.

Food Glorious Food.
Words and Music by Lionel Bart.

This Ole House.
Words and Music by Stuart Hamblen.

(I Can't Get No) Satisfaction.

Words and Music by Mick Jagger & Keith Richards.

From Russia With Love.
Words and Music by Lionel Bart.

Moderato

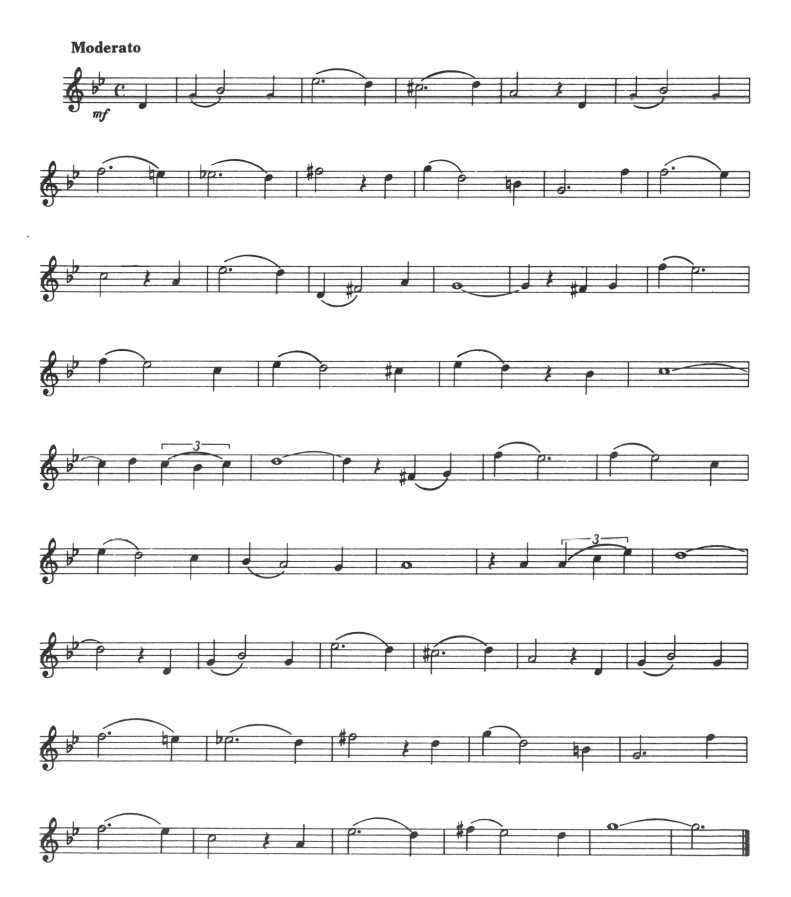

Who Will Buy.

Words and Music by Lionel Bart.

It's Not Unusual.

Words and Music by Gordon Mills & Les Reed.

Moderately, with a beat

How Insensitive.

Music by Antonio Carlos Jobim. Original lyrics by Vinicius De Moraes. English lyrics by Norman Gimbel.

Downtown.
Words and Music by Tony Hatch.

Ebb Tide.

Words by Carl Sigman. Music by Robert Maxwell.

Moderato

The Deadwood Stage (Whip-Crack-Away).

Words by Paul Francis Webster. Music by Sammy Fain.

With A Little Help From My Friends.

Words and Music by John Lennon & Paul McCartney.

Money, Money, Money.
Words and Music by Benny Andersson & Bjorn Ulvaeus.

Moderato

Waterloo.
Words and Music by Benny Andersson, Stig Anderson and Bjorn Ulvaeus.

The Magnificent Seven.
Music by Elmer Bernstein.

Moderately with vigour

The James Bond Theme.
By John Barry.

Moderato

The Entertainer
Scott Joplin

Dancing Queen.
Words and Music by Benny Andersson, Stig Anderson & Bjorn Ulvaeus.

The Girl From Ipanema (Garota De Ipanema).

Music by Antonio Carlos Jobim. Original words by Vinicius De Moraes. English lyric by Norman Gimbel.

Bluesette.

Words by Norman Gimbel. Music by Jean Thielemans.

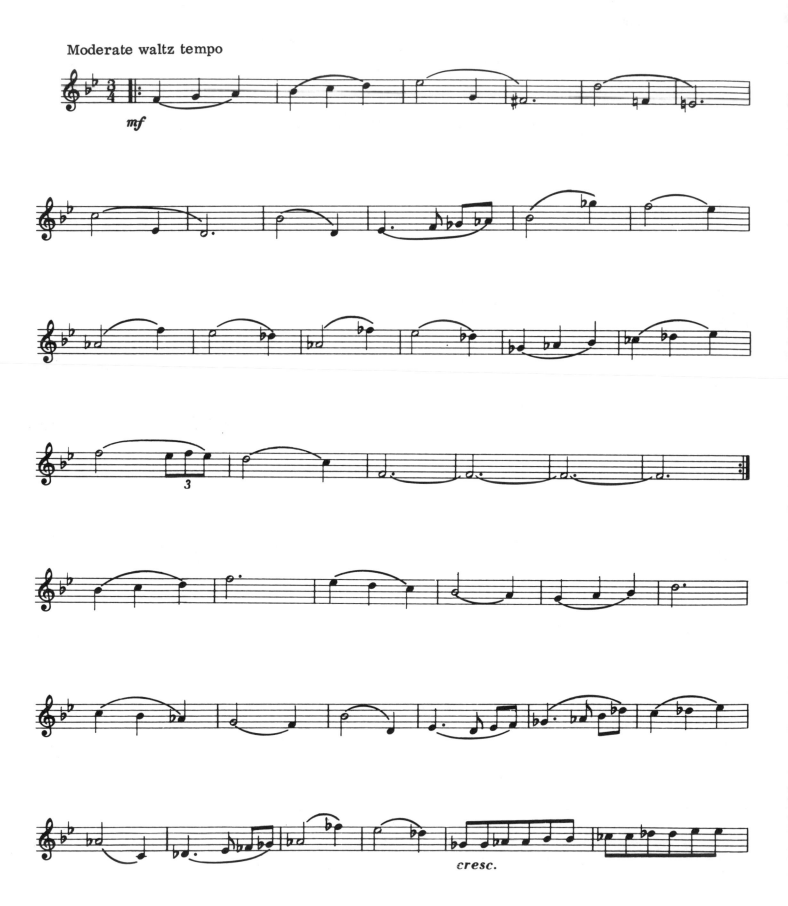

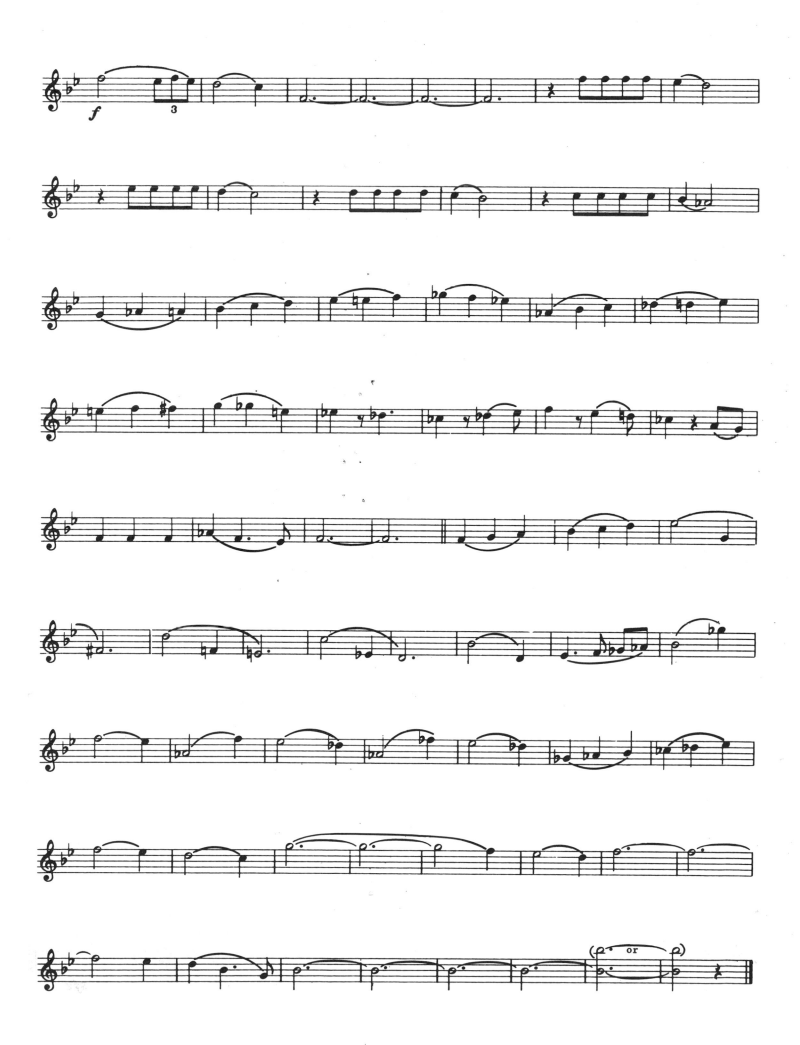

Tuxedo Junction.
Words by Buddy Feyne. Music by Erskine Hawkins, William Johnson & Julian Dash.

Take Five.
Music by Paul Desmond.

The Peanut Vendor.

Words by Marion Sunshine & L. Wolfe Gilbert. Music by Moises Simons.

Bright Latin Beat

Nola

Traditional

Mood Indigo.

Words and Music by Duke Ellington, Irving Mills & Albany Bigard.

Mambo Jambo.
Words by Raymond Karl & Charlie Towne. Music by Perez Prado.

Lazy River.

Words and Music by Hoagy Carmichael & Sidney Arodin.

Moderato

Hawaii Five-O.
By Mort Stevens.

With a driving beat

Live And Let Die.
Words and Music by Paul McCartney.

Lawrence of Arabia.
By Maurice Jarre.

Tico Tico.

Words by Ervin Drake. Music by Zequinha Abreu.

9/95(22420)